# Bears! Bears! Bears!

**Good Fun for Great Kids**

A Planet Dexter, Jr. Book

The Editors of Planet Dexter

PLANET DEXTER

**Scholastic Inc.**

New York  Toronto  London  Auckland  Sydney

## Acknowledgments

Louise Colligan, Nancy White, and the School Works Team

## And Now a Message from Our Corporate Lawyer

ISBN 0-590-97222-7

Copyright © 1996 by The Editors of Planet Dexter.
Text Development and Production by School Works.
Interior Text Design and Illustrations by Claude Martinot. Cover art by Claude Martinot.
All rights reserved. Published by Scholastic Inc., 555 Broadway, New York, NY 10012, by arrangement with Addison-Wesley Publishing Company.

12 11 10 9 8 7 6 5 4 3 2 1        6 7 8 9/9 0 1/0

Printed in the U.S.A.                    08

First Scholastic printing, October 1996

# THE BEAR FACTS

**W**elcome to Planet Dexter. In case you didn't know, it's the place where kids' brains hold twice as much, and they can do just about anything. It's also a place where learning just might happen while everyone's having a great time.

So why on Earth have eighteen lovable counting bears landed on Planet Dexter? So kids can have eighteen lovable friends to play with. And while they're playing, children can also—

| | |
|---|---|
| explore | count |
| classify | add and subtract |
| compare | multiply and divide |
| measure | make patterns |
| estimate | solve word problems |

**I**t's a well-known fact that children and bear cubs have a lot in common—they both like to climb trees and cuddle. But human children are way ahead of bears in some areas, like hand-eye coordination and small motor skills. The four-to-seven year old bunch especially love to handle small objects like cute little teddy bears. This "paws-on" practice provides valuable experience for later on when they'll learn to read and write—and operate the VCR for their parents. So go ahead and take out the bears. Having eighteen colorful plastic bears in your house is going to be terrific—even if some of them wind up under the sofa cushions, in the vacuum cleaner bag, or under the bed!

3

**K**ids will love hanging around with Planet Dexter's counting bears on the floor, bed, or kitchen table...or at the campground or beach—any time or place where they want something fun to do. With the help of **Bears! Bears! Bears!** (which is authored by a team of really laid back, nice people who are also educators and parents), kids will discover lots of ingenious ways to play with the bears. And if it happens that kids also pick up some math, reading, and thinking skills along the way, great.

**W**hen your child sees this funny looking shape, he or she should place the bear, standing up, right over the outline.

**T**his bigger outline means the bear should be lying on its back.

# How to Use This Book

**S**ome of the pages in this book suggest games and activities for you and your child to do together. The directions on these "teamwork" pages are written just for you. (You'll recognize these pages right away by the picture of the adult and baby bear reading together.)

**P**rofessor Bear will tell you which skill your child is learning on each page.

**T**he Teddy Bear signifies a "kid page." Kid pages have directions that are written for kids, usually "spoken" by a character on that page. You can read the directions aloud if your child hasn't started reading. Yes, it does mean you have to pretend to be a bear lifeguard or a bear movie usher, but, hey, your child will be busy pretending plastic bears are out boating or going to the movies!

**O**ne more thing. Please remember that the real value of *Bears! Bears! Bears!* is the opportunity it provides to play around with a kid, having fun *that happens to be of educational value*, while at home, school, on the beach, stuck in a car, or just about anywhere.

**I**f you have ideas of your own about *Bears! Bears! Bears!* we'd like to hear them—really! Here's our address:

The Editors of Planet Dexter
**Addison-Wesley Publishing Company**
One Jacob Way
Reading, MA  01867

**O**r you can fax us at (617) 944-8243 or even contact us via the Internet at pdexter@aw.com
or America Online at PDexter.

5

# Meet the Bears

Make way for bears! Push the coffee table against the wall—and the ottoman too. Your child will want lots of space to spread out the 18 counting bears who've joined your family. Give your child plenty of time to play with the bears, scoop them up, make up bear stories, or just hide them under the rug.

After a while, or maybe on another day, mention that you know a few games to try with the bears.

TWO YELLOW BEARS ARE SLEEPING NEXT TO AUNT TILLIE'S WASTE-BASKET.

## Wake Up the Bears

Hide the bears around the house. Tell your child the bears have been sleeping all winter, and it's time to wake them up. Give your child color and direction clues to find the sleeping bears. Keep going until your child wakes up all the bears.

## Bears Make a Racket

Find a metal container—Aunt Tillie's tin wastebasket, an old aluminum saucepan, even a metal pie plate will do. Ask your child to count each bear as you drop it in the container with a nice loud bang. If your child skips a number, just say it out loud and keep right on going. Then switch. One by one, take out the bears and see if your child can count backwards. Or you do the counting while your child removes the bears.

BANG    ONE!

6

## Odd Bear Out

Ask your child to dump all 18 bears into a big pile, then pair them off (any color combination is fine). How many altogether? (18). Point out that when every bear has a partner, there's an *even* number of bears altogether.

Next round, have your child grab a handful of bears, arrange them into pairs again, and count all the bears in the group. Is there a bear without a partner? Then the total number of bears is an *odd* number. You can do this activity with any number of bears—or until you get tired of sitting on the floor!

## Compare Bears

Send your child around the house to measure objects in "bears." (Each bear is exactly one inch tall—or one inch long, lying down.) Your child will also enjoy measuring things with our bear ruler on the inside covers of this book.

FRED'S TAIL IS 10 BEARS LONG.

Exploring

# Teddy Bears Go

# to the Movies

Ten teddy bears are going to the movies. Will they all get seats? Count the seats and see. Put a teddy in each seat. How many have to wait on line for the next show?

Counting

# Bears Play Hide

**G**ood counting practice! Tell this story about the bears' hide-and-seek game while your child acts it out. Read the words in parentheses to let her know what to do. (Get ready by setting up some things for the bears to hide behind—a cereal box, the sugar bowl, whatever.)

READY OR NOT, HERE I COME!

YOU'RE IT!

**1.** Ten teddy bears are getting together for a game of hide-and-seek. (*Get 10 teddy bears together.*)

**2.** The last bear to yell, "Not It!" is It. (*Choose 1 bear to be It.*)

**3.** That bear covers its eyes while the other bears run away to hide. (*Find hiding places for 9 bears.*)

# and Seek

**4.** The bear who is It calls out, "Ready or not, here I come." Can you help find the bears' hiding places? (Each time you find a bear, count all the found bears. Then figure out how many bears are still hiding.)

**5.** Play the game again. The last bear to be found gets to be it.

Counting

# Bears Hit the

# Bear Family

Figuring out missing numbers helps
children understand how addition works.

2 + ? = 4

# Reunion

$$3 + ? = 6$$

$$2 + ? = 3$$

These families have lost their bear cubs. Put the bear cubs with their families. Which is the biggest family? The smallest?

Missing Numbers

# Eeny Meeny

**S**et up 10 bears in a circle.  Point to 1 bear as you say each word:

> Eeny meeny miney moe,
> catch a teddy by the toe.
> If he hollers, let him go,
> Eeny meeny miney moe!

**T**he last bear you point to is out of the game.  How many are left? Keep on going.  Count the bears after each round.  Last bear left is the winner.

# Miney Moe

Subtracting

# Teddy Bear

Counting by twos (and threes, fours, and on and on) gets kids ready to learn what multiplication is all about.

**1.** It's Teddy Bear Day. Do you want to have a bear parade? Get started by getting those bears in line. Let your child line up 1 bear of each color. Then count the bears. (There'll be 6.)

**2.** That's a pretty small parade. Let your child give each bear a matching partner. Count the rows of bears (there'll be 6 rows of 2). Then count the bears (12).

# Day Parade

**3.** What happens if the bears march in rows of 3? You've still got 6 rows, but now there are lots more bears—18 to be exact!

**4.** Now let your child go ahead and experiment with different numbers of bears in different numbers of rows.

TEDDY BEAR DAY PARADE

**C**ounting by **T**wos and **T**hrees

# Bears in Boats

**P**ut 1 bear in each boat. How many bears are in boats?
Put another bear in each boat. How many bears in boats, now?
What happens if you put 3 bears in each boat?
How about 4 bears? More bears?

# Up, Up, and

**T**welve bears are going up in a hot-air balloon! But they won't all fit in one basket. Divide the 12 bears into 2 equal groups. Put 1 group in each basket. How many bears in each basket? How many bears altogether?

# Away !

That was fun! Now the bears are going home. Divide the 12 bears so the same number of bears will be in each car.

Dividing

# Bears for Sale !

Playing with money introduces children to denominations and reinforces number skills. It's also fun!

**I**nvite your kids to play "Toy Store" with you. Tell them teddy bears are on sale today and give them a handful of pennies plus a few nickels, dimes, and quarters. Then open the store and let the sale begin!

**Y**ou start out as the sales person. You can say something like, "Would you like one of our beautiful red bears? They cost 25 cents each." Then help the kids pick out a quarter. The activity gets more complicated when you start selling orange and purple bears, which require a combination of dimes and nickels.

TEDDY BEARS' DEPARTMENT

1¢

5¢

24

**10¢** **15¢** **20¢** **25¢**

**A**ny bear of course, can be paid for with a combination of coins. If someone is out of dimes, for example, he can always use 10 pennies. If you want to get more advanced, you can even get into making change. See how it goes.

When you sell out, you can always play again.

Money

26

# Shape

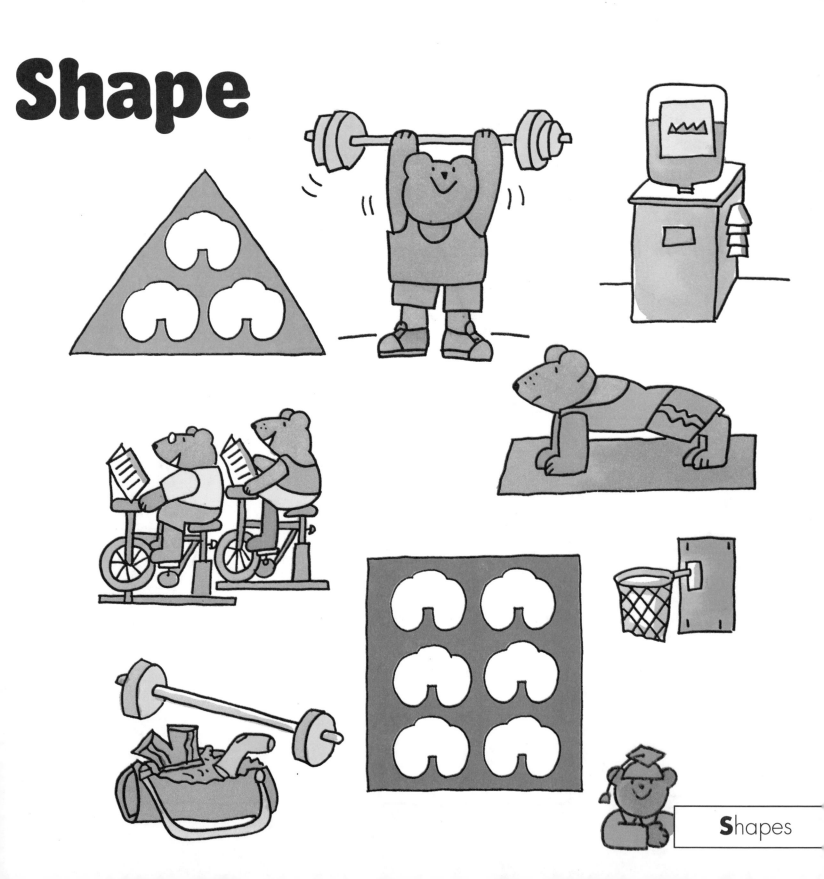

# A Tight Squeeze

Estimating

HERE COME THE BEARS. GUESS HOW MANY CAN STAND INSIDE EACH HONEY JAR? STAND THE NUMBER OF BEARS YOU GUESSED INSIDE EACH JAR. WERE YOU CLOSE?

# A Beary Nice Day

Let the kids use their bears—and their imaginations—to act out what 4 bear families did on a *beary* nice day at the park.

**O**ne day, 4 bear families had a nice day at the park—the Reds, the Blues, the Yellows, and the Greens. How many bears are in each family? How many bears went to the park?

**T**hey divided up into 2 teams for a relay race. How many bears on each team?

**E**ight bears played tag.
The rest went roller blading.
How many went roller blading?

**T**hey all played jump rope.
Two bears turned the rope.
One bear was jumping.
How many were on line to jump?

**S**tory **P**roblems

**T**wo bears climbed a tree.
Then 3 more bears climbed the tree.
How many bears were in the tree?

**T**hree bears played in the sandbox.
Each one made 2 sand castles.
How many castles did they make?

**O**ne of the bears said, "Let's all play kick ball." Two bears didn't feel like playing, but the rest of the bears did. How many bears were in the game? They chose 2 captains. The captains took turns choosing teams. How many bears were on each team?

**A**ll the bears are tired now. Time for a nap. They brought 4 blankets. How many bears took a nap on each blanket?

**S**weet dreams, bears!

Story Problems

# What Do Hungry

CAN YOU MAKE A GRAPH TO SHOW THE BEARS' FAVORITE FOODS? GATHER YOUR 18 BEARS. LOOK AT THE LIST. ON THE CHART, LINE UP THE RIGHT NUMBER OF BEARS TO SHOW HOW MANY LIKE EACH KIND OF FOOD.

| parsnips | bluefish | honey |

# Bears Eat ?

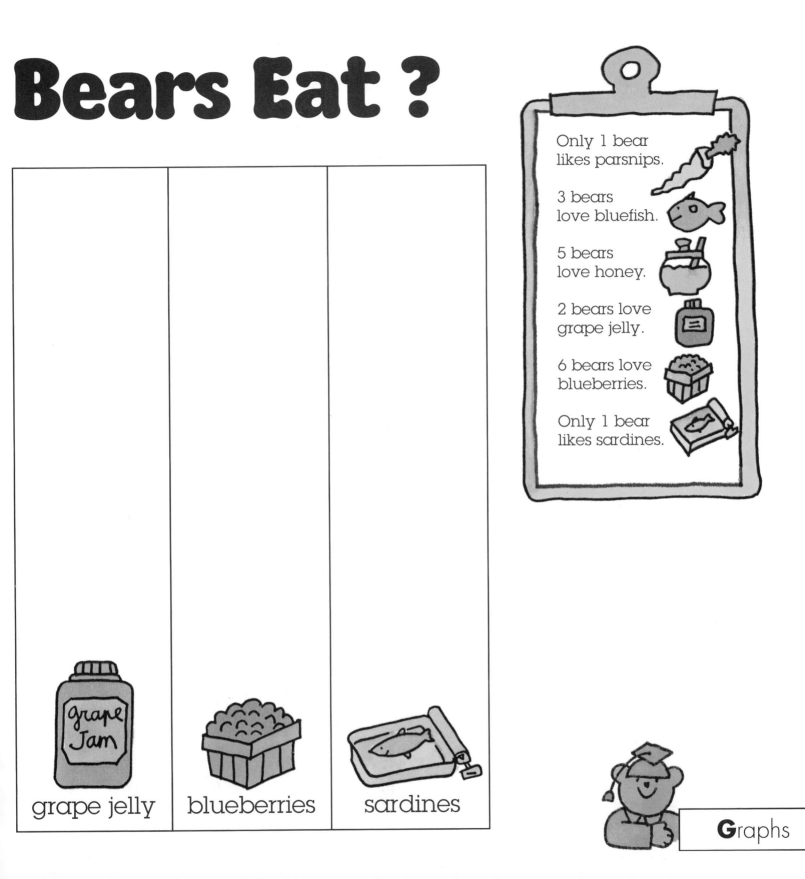

Only 1 bear likes parsnips.

3 bears love bluefish.

5 bears love honey.

2 bears love grape jelly.

6 bears love blueberries.

Only 1 bear likes sardines.

| grape jelly | blueberries | sardines |
| --- | --- | --- |

**G**raphs

# Lighten Up

HOW MANY BEARS DOES IT TAKE TO CHANGE A LIGHTBULB? STACK UP THE BEARS—LYING POSITION ONLY—UNDER EACH LIGHTBULB TO FIND OUT.

Measuring

# a Spot !

Patterns

# Baby Bear's

**M**ama and Papa Bear are making a quilt for Baby Bear. Lay your bears on the quilt to fill in the missing spaces.

# Quilt !

Here's another quilt for Baby Bear. Can you finish the pattern?

Patterns

# Bear Detectives

See if your children can be "bear detectives" and find the missing bears.

**WHERE DID THAT BEAR GET TO?**

**THAT PESKY BEAR!**

**G**et the kids to arrange all the bears in a big circle on the next page. Tell them to hide their eyes. No peeking while you take away 1 bear. Can the children guess which color bear is missing? After a few tries, take away 2, 3, or even more bears at a time. You can change the color arrangement, too.

**NOW WHERE IS THAT BEAR.**

**OKAY, BEARS, WE KNOW YOU'RE HERE!**

Logic

# Name Those

A real brain-teaser for
you and your kids!

**W**hat are the bears' names?
You can tell by what is in their
lunch boxes. Put the bears next to
their lunch boxes before you start.
(The answers are upside down in
the corner. But don't peek until
you try your hardest!)

**B**etty and Bonnie both have cookies.

**B**enny and Betty both have apples.

**B**arry and Becky both have honey.

**B**obby and Becky both have milk.

# Bears !

Logic

# 12 1/2 Things Kids
## (and Their Favorite Grown-Ups)
# Can Do With Counting Bears

**1.** Pick "Odds" or "Evens" with a partner. One of you grabs a handful of bears without counting. Throw them down. Then count the bears and see who won.

**2.** Guess how many bears you can stuff into your pocket. Then see if you were right.

**3.** Hide a bear in a silly place every day to see if somebody finds it. Good hiding places: a shoe, the medicine cabinet, under a pillow, Mom's briefcase, inside a hat, glove, or pocket.

**4.** Play "Simon Says." Make a color pattern with the bears, point to the pattern, and say: "Simon says: Do this!" See if a playmate can copy your pattern. (Hint: Make sure to leave half the bears for your partner to use.)

**5.** Put the bears in a bag. Ten times in a row, pick out 5 bears from the bag, then dump them back. Make a graph to show which colors you picked on each turn.

**6.** Close your eyes and pick a bear out of the pile. How many objects around the house can you find that are the same color as that bear?

**7.** Make a class of bears with a bear teacher. Act out a scene that happened at bear school.

**8.** You don't need jacks to play jacks. Use bears instead!

**9.** Put a bunch of bears in a coffee can. See if your partner can guess how many bears are inside by shaking the can.

**10.** Have a teddy-bear tea party...or a teddy-bear Little League game.

**11.** Make a seesaw with a ruler balanced across a spool of thread. See how many bears you can balance on the seesaw.

**12.** Clean-up time. Scoop up all the bears with both hands and put them away. How many scoops did it take?

**12 1/2.** Clean-up time again. Pour out all the bears, but this time scoop them up with one hand and put them away. How many one-handed scoops?